This book belongs to

C000184736

_____

I was _____ years old during the beginning
of the Coronavirus pandemic.

Pearls and Ink Publishing
© 2021 by Tahmina Ahmed

All rights reserved. No part of this publication may
be reproduced, without the prior written permission of
the copyright owner, except for the use of quotations.

Book design by Chakib Azzaoui

Hardcover ISBN: 978-1-8384032-0-1
Paperback ISBN: 978-1-8384032-1-8

Published by Pearls and Ink Publishing
www.pearlsandink.com

To my dear niece, Maryam. May Allāh forever bless you, protect you, and make you a beacon of light.

All praise is due to Allāh, the all-Kind, the Magnificent. It is He who blesses us with opportunities and it is He who instils success within them. We pray that He keeps our intentions sincere, grants us acceptance, and allows us to strive for excellence in all that we do for Him.

Special appreciation to my parents, husband and siblings, for all their support in helping me attain this goal.

Our dear, honourable teacher, Shaykh Yunus, whose uplifting and spiritual nurturing has been life-changing.

And my beloved mentor, Hanaa' Ibtes, whose priceless advice helped me to strive for my potential in all situations.

May Allah (swt) preserve them all.

Maryam in LOCKDOWN

Written by Tahmina Ahmed
Illustrated by Faisal Tahir

When tiny **little germs** were invading the air,
it wasn't safe for little Maryam to go near.

A big illness called 'Corona' was making people sick,
but staying indoors to be **safe** was the trick.

Maryam was **upset,** as she couldn't go to town, and now she had to be in something called '**lockdown.**'

But Mummy told Maryam **not to be sad,**

and instead of going out she could **pray** with her Dad.

Maryam noticed Daddy didn't go to the **mosque to pray**.

Instead, he was praying where Maryam likes to play.

Daddy explained that germs could **spread** in the mosque by many,

so he's **praying at home** and then will call up her Granny.

Maryam asked if she could go and visit **Granny** instead,

"the lockdown is making me feel bored," she said.

But Daddy said that Granny
is too **weak and old**,

"the germs could hurt her
quicker," by the doctor she
was told.

So it was better for Maryam to speak over the **phone**,

and that way Granny would **not feel alone**.

Then, Maryam wanted to go next-door to play,
with her **friend Musa** who she plays with every day.

But Maryam realised that **germs** can still spread, so she went to make Musa a **nice card** instead.

When Maryam wanted to leave her home for **fresh air**, she **played in the garden** with her teddy bear.

When Maryam was missing her **school** and **friends**,

she still did her schoolwork and played during weekends.

Maryam missed her Arabic teacher, so began to **worry**.

She missed learning her letters and **Islamic stories**.

Happy, yet down, Maryam asked if Corona would **go away**.
Mummy said, "not for long, insha'Allah, a **cure** is on its way!"

Holloway News — Scientists work on Covid-19 vacc

Mummy also said "to **Allah** we should always **pray**, that He takes away Corona and keeps us safe every day."

Then, Maryam said she has something **very important** to say.

She said, "the lockdown has made me love **Allah** in many ways!"

Mummy asked Maryam why she loves **Allah** now more,
as when **lockdown** first started, she wasn't as happy as before.

Maryam said, "I **realised** that Allah has **gifted** me lots in life. Good friends, good food, and great family ties!"

And most of all she's learnt you should be **thankful** if you're safe,
and cherish **Allah's blessings** with love and faith!

"Do not lose hope, nor be sad" [3:139]

"And He has made me blessed wherever I am" [19:31]